Debra Eason

D1361506

ESSENTIALS

GCSE Design & Technology
Textiles Technology
Workbook

Contents

Product Considerations

4   The Need for Textiles

5   Equipment and Tools

8   Research

12   Specifications

13   Colour and Design

Environmental Factors

16   Textiles and the Environment

18   Designer Responsibility

19   Recycling

20   Ethical Goods

Designing

22   Sketch Books and Mood Boards

23   Trends

24   Designing

28   Product Specification

29   Manufacturing Specification

Materials & Components

30   Fibres and Yarns

31   Fabrics

36   Properties of Fibres and Fabrics

38   Finishes

42   Components

43   Smart Materials and Technical Textiles

Contents

Modelling and Construction

46 Modelling Colour and Decoration

50 Modelling Fabrics

51 Modelling with ICT

52 Pattern Making

53 Toiles

54 Construction Techniques

Safety and Standards

56 Quality Control

57 Testing Textiles

58 Regulations and Standards

60 Health and Safety

Manufacturing

62 Planning Production

65 Computers in the Textile Industry

68 Industrial Clothing Manufacture

Advertising and Marketing

70 Advertising and Marketing

71 Packaging

72 Labelling

Exam-Style Questions

74 Exam-Style Questions

94 Notes

The Need for Textiles

Textiles

1 Which of the following statements provides the best definition for the term **'textiles'**? Tick the correct option.

    A The group name for fabrics constructed from woven strands of yarn. ⬜

    B An alternative name for soft furnishings. ⬜

    C A general term used to describe any product that is made from fabric. ⬜

    D A scientific term for fibres that can be made into fabrics. ⬜

2 The table contains four functions of textile products.

Match the products **A, B, C** and **D** with the functions **1–4** in the table. Enter the appropriate number in the boxes provided.

    A Bed linen ⬜

    B Hats ⬜

    C Wall hangings ⬜

    D Teddy bears ⬜

	Function
1	Protection
2	Decoration
3	Comfort
4	Entertainment

3 Which of the following items are examples of textile products? Tick the correct options.

    A Armchair ⬜   **B** Cup and saucer ⬜

    C Carpet ⬜   **D** Horse blanket ⬜

    E Pair of slippers ⬜   **F** Vase ⬜

    G Tent ⬜

4 Unscramble the letters below to find three different categories of fabric.

    a) ENVOW _____   **b)** BEDNOD _____

    c) KIDTENT _____

Advanced Uses

5 List four different industries that use textiles in advanced applications.

    a) _____   **b)** _____

    c) _____   **d)** _____

Specialist Equipment and Tools

1 What is a **component**? Tick the correct option.

A   A tool used to make a textile product. ◯

B   An item that is incorporated into the final product. ◯

C   A piece of computerised machinery. ◯

D   A chemical treatment. ◯

2 Fill in the missing words to complete the following sentence.

Specialist tools and pieces of equipment have special _____ that allow you to carry

out a specific _____ correctly and efficiently.

3 What scale of production are the tools and equipment commonly used in schools best suited for?

_____

Colour and Design Equipment

4 The table contains different types of colour and design equipment.

Match descriptions **A, B, C** and **D** with the equipment **1–4** in the table. Enter the appropriate number in the boxes provided.

A   Heat resistant jars that are used to melt wax. ◯

B   A tool that is used to push pigment through a screen onto fabric. ◯

C   Dyes in solid form that can be used on both synthetic and natural fabrics. ◯

D   A tool that is used to apply hot wax to fabrics. ◯

	Equipment
1	Fabric crayons and pens
2	Batik pot
3	Squeegee
4	Tjanting

Pressing Equipment

5 Choose the correct words from the options given to complete the following sentences.

effects   heat press   transfer   pleat

A _____ is a machine that can be used to _____ printed

designs from special paper onto fabrics. It can also be used to _____ fabrics ◯

and create special _____ .

Equipment and Tools

Machines

1 Alongside each piece of machinery below, write **joining** if it is used to join pieces of fabric or **constructing** if it is used to make pieces of fabric.

a) Sewing machine ....

b) Weaving loom ....

c) Knitting machine ....

d) Overlocker ....

2 The table contains four types of sewing machine.

Match descriptions **A, B, C** and **D** with the machines **1−4** in the table. Enter the appropriate number in the boxes provided.

A Controlled by a computer interface. ◯

B Used to join fabrics and do simple embroidery. ◯

C Used for joining and finishing at the same time. ◯

D Can create lots of different decorative stitches. ◯

	Machines
1	Overlocker
2	Standard sewing machine
3	Embroidery machine
4	Computerised sewing machine

3 How can you speed up the production of knitted products using a knitting machine?
Tick the correct option.

A Recycle fabrics ◯   **B** Employ cheaper labour ◯

C Give better instructions ◯   **D** Link the machine to a computer ◯

4 The picture below is of a weaving loom. List four different types of weaving looms

a) ....

b) ....

c) ....

d) ....

Non-Machine Based Equipment

1 Which of the following pieces of equipment are used to obtain the correct size and fit for a garment? Tick the correct options.

A Tape measure ◯ **B** Overlocker ◯

C Pinking shears ◯ **D** Mannequin ◯

E Embroidery frame ◯

2 Choose the correct words from the options given to complete the following sentences.

| decorative | prevent | pinking | edges | serrated |

_____ shears have _____ edges for finishing off the

_____ of fabric to _____ fraying. They also produce

_____ edges.

3 The table contains four different tools used to make textile products.

Match descriptions **A, B, C** and **D** with the tools **1–4** in the table. Enter the appropriate number in the boxes provided.

A Cut fabric ◯

B Holds fabric in place whilst decorative stitching is applied ◯

C Prevent fraying ◯

D Temporarily hold fabric pieces together ◯

	Tools
1	Pins
2	Scissors
3	Pinking shears
4	Embroidery frame

4 Unscramble the letters to find two other pieces of non-machine based equipment you might come across.

a) AIRLOST HALCK _____ **b)** EELDEN _____

5 Why are tape measures often better suited to textile applications than rulers? Tick the correct options.

A They are cheaper. ◯

B They can be curved easily. ◯

C They are longer. ◯

D They are available in different colours. ◯

E They can be used to measure inches and centimetres. ◯

Research

The Purpose of Research

1 Choose the correct words from the options given to complete the following sentences.

> **information**　　　**analyse**　　　**findings**　　　**collating**

Research involves collecting and .... (gathering together) ....

You then need to .... it and report the ....

2 Which of the following statements provide valid reasons for conducting research?
Tick the correct options.

A　To identify factors that will affect a consumer's purchasing decision.　◯

B　To help develop your communication skills.　◯

C　To find out the preferences of your target market.　◯

D　To help you make decisions about your design.　◯

E　To give you an opportunity to get out of the classroom and talk to people.　◯

F　You like drawing charts and graphs.　◯

Primary Research

3 Are the following statements about primary research **true** or **false**?

a)　Primary research involves information gathered only from the Internet. ....

b)　Questionnaires and surveys are the most popular methods for collecting consumer information.

....

c)　Books are a good source of information for primary research. ....

d)　Telephone conversations can help you obtain information directly from members of your target market.

....

4 Circle the correct options to complete the following sentences.

a)　Questionnaires need a **large / small** sample size to produce reliable results.

b)　General surveys target a **specific / random** cross-section of society.

c)　The questions in surveys need to be **ambiguous / focused**.

d)　Surveys should avoid **closed / leading** questions and include lots of **closed / leading** questions.　◯

Primary Research (Cont.)

1 Which of the following methods of research is best suited to finding out about new styles and trends? Tick the correct option.

A Conducting a questionnaire ◯ **B** Looking at library books ◯

C Attending a show or exhibition ◯ **D** Holding a focus group ◯

2 Who is normally involved in a focus group? Tick the correct option.

A A team of designers ◯ **B** The client, designer and manufacturer ◯

C A group of children of different ages ◯ **D** A small group of consumers ◯

3 **A, B** and **C** are examples of different types of question formats. Read them carefully and then answer the questions below.

A Is price important to you? No [ ] Yes [ ] Sometimes [ ]

B What price would you be prepared to pay for this product?

C Wouldn't you agree that this product is better than similar products on the market?

i) Which question is an example of an open question? ◯

ii) Which question is an example of a leading question? ◯

iii) Which question is an example of a closed question? ◯

iv) Which question is in the format that is most useful in a focused questionnaire? ◯

Secondary Research

4 Which of the following examples are sources of secondary information? Tick the correct options.

A Newspapers ◯ **B** Questionnaires ◯

C Trade publications ◯ **D** Interviews ◯

E Market reports ◯

Inspiration for Design

5 Other than art, photographs, materials and fabrics, name four possible sources of inspiration for designers.

a) .... b) ....

c) .... d) .... ▢

Research

Product Analysis

1 What does **disassemble** mean? Tick the correct option.

A To gather together ☐   **B** To make a judgement ☐

C To take apart ☐   **D** To deactivate ☐

2 What is the main purpose of disassembly as part of product analysis? Tick the correct option.

A To recycle the materials and components ☐

B To identify the key features of the product ☐

C To practise your practical skills ☐

D To help get rid of competitors' products ☐

3 Briefly explain how product analysis can help a designer.

....

....

4 Unscramble the letters to find the three main processes that you need to go through as part of product analysis.

a) ANYSEAL ....   **b)** SASSES ....

c) TIDYFINE ....

5 Choose the correct 'f' word from the options given to complete each of the following questions. You should try to answer these questions as part of your product analysis.

     finishes   **features**   **fabric**   **fibre**   **function**

a) What is the .... of the product?

b) What is the .... content of the fabric used?

c) What are the key design .... ?

d) How has the .... been constructed?

e) What .... have been applied?

6 List three factors beginning with 'e' that you need to consider when carrying out product analysis.

a) ....   **b)** ....   **c)** ....   ☐

Industrial Practices

1 What is **intelligence gathering**? Tick the correct options.

A Finding clever people to take part in focus groups ◯

B Collecting detailed information about the target market ◯

C Monitoring high-street trends ◯

D Detailed product analysis ◯

2 Number the following processes **1–4** to show the order in which they are carried out in the textile industry.

A Consumer surveys and focus groups are used to find out what consumers think of the idea. ◯

B Intelligence gathering is carried out. ◯

C The client briefs the designer. ◯

D The designer develops their ideas. ◯

Analysing and Evaluating

3 The table contains four methods of presenting research findings.

Match the requirements **A, B, C** and **D** to the methods of presentation **1–4** in the table. Enter the appropriate number in the boxes provided.

A An easy way of comparing the popularity of three different design ideas, based on the percentage of consumers who chose each design as their favourite. ◯

B A visual summary of the colours, shapes, textures, etc. preferred by the target market. ◯

C The results of a survey in which 50 people were asked to indicate how much they would be prepared to pay for a particular product by choosing one of five price ranges. ◯

D A comparison between the properties of different fabrics and a profile for the 'ideal' fabric. ◯

	Method of Presentation
1	Star profile
2	Pie chart
3	Bar chart / histogram
4	Mood board

4 Label each diagram below with the name of the type of chart it shows.

a)

....

b)

....

◻

Specifications

Specifications

1 The table contains three different types of specification.

Match descriptions **A, B** and **C** with the types of specification **1–3** in the table. Enter the appropriate number in the boxes provided.

A Produced when the product has undergone final modifications. ◯

B Created from the design brief and research findings; sets out the essential and desirable criteria. ◯

C Identifies all the materials, tools and processes needed to produce a prototype. ◯

	Type of Specification
1	Design
2	Product
3	Manufacturing

2 There are a number of factors that need to be considered when producing a design specification. Draw a line to match each factor to the appropriate question.

Form

Materials and components

Scale of production

Function

What does the product need to do?

What shape does the product need to be?

What will the product be made from?

How many do you need to produce?

Design Specification

3 Are the following statements about design specifications true or false? Circle the correct option.

a) They normally take the form of a flow chart. **TRUE / FALSE**

b) They include all the key points from the brief. **TRUE / FALSE**

c) They are written after research has been carried out. **TRUE / FALSE**

d) They include detailed information about production processes. **TRUE / FALSE**

e) They are used to help you focus your design ideas. **TRUE / FALSE**

Colour

1 Fill in the missing names and terms relating to colour.

a) | Yellow | **+** | | **=** | Green |

b) Green is a _____ colour.

c) | Primary | **+** | Secondary | **=** | |

2 How do you produce a tertiary colour?

_____

Describing Colour

3 The table contains three terms used to describe colours.

Match descriptions **A**, **B** and **C** with the terms **1–3** in the table. Enter the appropriate number in the boxes provided.

A Colours that work well together ⬭

B Contrasting colours on opposite sides of the colour wheel ⬭

C Shades, tones and tints of a single colour ⬭

	Terms
1	Harmonious
2	Monochromatic
3	Complementary

4 a) Give one example of a pair of complementary colours.

_____

b) Give one example of a pair of harmonious colours.

_____

c) Give one example of a 'warm' colour.

_____

d) Give one example of a 'cold' colour.

_____

Colour and Design

1 Draw a line to match each term to the correct description.

Hue	Produced by adding white to a colour.
Tone	The specific colour that you see, e.g. crimson or royal blue.
Shade	Usually refers to a hue that has been darkened by mixing it with black.
Tint	Refers to how light or dark the hue is.

2 Think about how the target market for a product might affect your choice of colours.
For each product below, suggest a palette of three colours that you think would be appropriate.

a) A clothing range for toddlers, i.e. children of 2–3 years of age.

b) A product to be used by business professionals in the workplace.

c) A range of soft furnishings for traditional country lifestyles.

3 Suggest one factor, other than the target market, that might influence your choice of colours.

4 Circle the correct options in the following sentences.

a) The appearance of a colour is affected by the intensity and type of light, e.g. bright colours look **more / less** intense in direct sunlight.

b) Colours can have different effects against different skin tones, e.g. some warm colours work well with **dark / pale** skin but not with **pale / dark** skin.

c) Colours have **the same / different** symbolic meanings in different cultures.

Colour and Design

Pattern and Texture

1 Choose the correct words from the options given to complete the following sentences.

style   scale   regular   texture   irregular   graphic

a) A pattern that is uniform or repeats itself is called a _____ pattern.

b) A pattern that is completely random and does not repeat itself is called _____.

c) It is important to consider the _____ of a pattern or design, i.e. the size of the pattern or design in relation to the size of the product.

d) _____ affects the handle and feel of a fabric, but it can also be used to add interest to a design.

Line and Style

2 Draw a line to match each type of line to the effect it will produce.

Vertical lines		Can be used to create dramatic effects.
Diagonal lines		Make things look tall and narrow, e.g. have a slimming effect.
Horizontal lines		Make things look short and wide.

3 Which of the following statements provides the best definition for **style**? Tick the correct option.

A The visual effect created by the colour palette.

B The shape and form of the product.

C The period or design movement that influenced the design.

D The overall effect created by a combination of different visual elements.

4 Fill in the missing words to complete the following sentences.

a) Different styles are often associated with different _____ in time.

b) Many _____ develop their own distinctive style.

Textiles and the Environment

The Impact of Textiles on the Environment

1 Which of the following statements help to explain why textile products have such a large impact on the environment? Tick the correct options.

A Energy is needed to manufacture, transport and maintain the products.

B Some textile products don't require any / much packaging.

C Natural resources are used to provide some of the materials for the products.

D Natural resources are used in various manufacturing processes.

E Many of the materials used to make the products are recyclable.

F Waste is produced by various manufacturing processes.

Manufacturing Textiles and Sustainability

2 Name two stages in the production of textile products that involve chemical processes.

a) ....   **b)** ....

3 What are the main waste products produced by dyeing processes? Tick the correct options.

A Contaminated water   **B** Plastic molecules

C Chemical waste   **D** Bleach

E Enzymes   **F** Fabric selvedge

4 Circle the correct word from the options given in the following sentences.

a) Cold water dyeing processes require **more / less** energy.

b) Identifying fabrics that already have the required properties can **reduce / increase** the need for chemical finishes.

c) **Natural / Chemical** dyes produced from sustainable sources have less impact on the environment than **natural / chemical** dyes.

d) **Light / Dark** dyes contaminate greater volumes of water because the fabrics require more rinsing.

e) Working with a yarn's natural colour **increases / eliminates** the need for bleach or dyes.

Laundry and Aftercare   AQA • OCR

5 Name three aftercare processes that **use energy**.

a) ....   **b)** ....   **c)** ....

Laundry and Aftercare (Cont.)   AQA • OCR

6 Fill in the missing words to complete the following sentences.

a) Energy is saved by using fabrics that can be washed at _____ temperatures.

b) Fabrics and products that are durable and well made will have a _____ life span.

c) Less energy is required to care for crease-resistant fabrics as they don't need _____ .

Waste Textiles

7 How does computerised lay planning and pattern cutting help to reduce waste?

_____

_____

8 Fabric scraps are reused within the automotive industry as filling for car seats. What other items can be produced from this type of waste? Tick the correct option.

A Bandages ⬡   **B** T-shirts ⬡

C Upholstery ⬡   **D** Emergency blankets ⬡

Designer Obsolescence and Disposal

9 a) Which statement provides the best definition for **design obsolescence**?
Tick the correct option.

A A timeless design that will ensure the product has a long life span. ⬡

B A design that will become outdated and be replaced despite the product still being functional. ⬡

C A design that avoids fashions and trends that are likely to change quickly. ⬡

D A design that takes into account ergonomics and anthropometrics. ⬡

b) Why is design obsolescence an environmental issue?

_____

_____

10 What happens to most products that are thrown out as general refuse? Tick the correct options.

A They are recycled. ⬡   **B** They are incinerated. ⬡

C They are reused. ⬡   **D** They are put into landfill sites. ⬡

Designer Responsibility

Reducing Environmental Impact

1 How can design obsolescence be avoided?

_____

2 For each pair of products, underline the product that has the lowest environmental impact.

a) towelling nappies / disposable paper nappies

b) a classically tailored black dress / a fashionable cocktail dress in the latest style

3 Below is a basic fabric specification.
Circle the correct options to ensure the specification is as environmentally friendly as possible.

Fabric specification:
- **organic / inorganic** cotton
- **bleached / unbleached / dyed**
- **dry clean only / machine wash at 90° / machine wash at 30°**

4 Why are electroplated components, like zips and buckles, an environmental concern?
Tick the correct option.

A Electroplating prevents rust so the components last longer. ☐

B Electroplated components cannot be reused easily. ☐

C The process of electroplating produces a toxic sludge. ☐

D Electroplated components have to be imported from abroad. ☐

5 Suggest two ways in which you could reduce the environmental impact of the components used in a design.

a) _____

b) _____

6 Suggest two ways in which you could reduce the environmental impact of the production process.

a) _____

b) _____

7 What information should be included on a product's label to help minimise its impact on the environment during and after end-use? Tick the correct options.

A Aftercare instructions ☐   **B** Barcode ☐

C Country of origin ☐   **D** Size ☐

E Recycling information ☐   **F** Company logo ☐

Recycling

1 **a)** What does this symbol mean? Tick the correct option.

A Put rubbish in the bin ☐

B Save energy ☐

C Made from recycled material ☐

D Can be recycled ☐

b) What is the name of this symbol? Tick the correct option.

A Energy efficiency symbol ☐   **B** Mobius loop ☐

C Fairtrade Mark ☐   **D** Green dot ☐

2 There are three main types of recycling: **primary**, **secondary** and **tertiary**.

a) Which type of recycling is being described in each of the statements below?

i) The product is physically broken down and reused in a different state. ....

ii) The materials are broken down and reformulated using chemicals. ....

iii) The textile product can be reused as it is; no further processing is needed. ....

b) Give one example for each type of recycling.

i) Example of Primary Recycling: ....

ii) Example of Secondary Recycling: ....

iii) Example of Tertiary Recycling: ....

The Importance of Recycling

3 Fill in the missing words to complete the following sentences.

a) Textiles products use a lot of .... resources, so it is important to

.... the materials rather than let them go to waste.

b) The key reasons for recycling are to save ...., conserve raw

.... and .... the impact of production on the ☐

environment.

Recycling and Ethical Goods

The 6 'R's of Recycling   OCR

1 a) What are the 6 'R's of recycling?

i) _____   ii) _____   iii) _____

iv) _____   v) _____   vi) _____

b) Use your answers to part a) to fill in the missing words and complete the sentences below.

i) Take old products apart and _____ the materials in new ones.

ii) _____ damaged products instead of buying new ones.

iii) _____ to buy products that are not sustainable.

iv) _____ all materials that can be recycled.

v) _____ your design ideas with the 6 'R's in mind.

vi) _____ the carbon footprint of a product.

Ethical Goods   AQA • OCR

2 What are **ethical goods**? Tick the correct option.

A Goods that are produced in a way that does not compromise human rights or the environment. ◯

B Goods that are expensive to buy but are of a very high quality. ◯

C Goods that are influenced by different cultures. ◯

D Goods for which part of the sale price goes to charity. ◯

3 The choices that you make as a consumer, when you buy products, have an impact on other people.

a) Name one group of people who might be affected by your choice.

_____

b) Briefly explain how your choice can have an effect on them.

_____

_____

Ethical Goods (Cont.)　　　AQA • OCR

1 What does this symbol represent? Tick the correct option.

A Recyclable ⬜

B Sustainable ⬜

C Fairtrade ⬜

D Free from harmful products ⬜

2 Draw lines to match the type of label or symbol to the correct description.

Oeko-Tex® label	Assures that the wood fibres used in the product come from carefully managed forests.
FSC logo	Shows the energy efficiency of appliances like washing machines and tumble driers.
Fairtrade Mark	Assures that the product has been tested and it is free from harmful substances.
European energy label	Assures that the Third World producers were paid a fair and stable price.

3 For each of the following descriptions, sketch the appropriate symbol.

a) This product contains 30% recycled materials.

b) This product is made from recyclable PET (Polyethylene Terepthalate).

4 Circle the correct options to complete the sentences below.

The label above is a **European /Environmental** Eco Label. It is applied to products where steps have been taken to **minimise /maximise** their environmental impact over their whole life-cycle. ⬜

Sketchbooks and Mood Boards

Using Sketchbooks AQA

1 What type of images should you put in a sketchbook? Tick the correct option.

A   Quick sketches of initial ideas and inspirational images ◯

B   Working drawings ◯

C   Detailed technical drawings ◯

D   Photographs of your prototype in production ◯

Mood Boards AQA • OCR

2 Choose the correct words from the options given to complete the following sentences.

style   display   information   textures   visual

A mood board brings together a variety of _____ focused on a particular theme and

presented on a _____ board. The images usually reflect the 'here and now' and are

meant to provide a _____ summary of your ideas and research. By using a range of

_____, patterns and colours you can communicate the overall

_____ or 'feel' that you are aiming for.

3 What type of information would you expect to find on a mood board? Tick the correct options.

A   Colour swatches ◯   B   Fabric swatches ◯

C   Working drawings ◯   D   Photographs and images ◯

E   Tables, graphs and charts ◯ F   Detailed written information ◯

Using Mood Boards AQA • OCR

4 Which of the following statements describe appropriate uses for mood boards? Tick the correct options.

A   To help finalise a palette of colours, textures and patterns. ◯

B   To help communicate your ideas and research to other people. ◯

C   To show the different stages of production. ◯

D   As a discussion point to help clarify consumer preferences. ◯

E   To show the development process that you went through. ◯

F   To develop styles for garments and products. ◯

Trend Forecasting

AQA • OCR

1 What is meant by the term **trend**? Tick the correct option.

A A specific product ⬜ **B** A lifestyle ⬜

C A fashion or fad ⬜ **D** Popular culture ⬜

2 What is the main difference between a mood board and a trend board?

....

3 Choose the correct words from the options given to complete this explanation of the difference between a trend board and a trend book.

different products summary trends data event reference purposes general similar specific

Trend boards and trend books have different .... A trend board is

.... to a mood board. It provides a visual .... of a

.... trend and is usually created for an ...., like an exhibition

or client presentation. A trend book is used for .... when designing and

developing new .... It contains .... and images for lots of

different ....

4 In the fashion industry, how long before the garments are sold do the designers begin putting together ideas? Tick the correct option.

A Two days ⬜ **B** Two weeks ⬜

C Two months ⬜ **D** Two or more years ⬜

5 Unscramble the letters below to find some of the areas that specialist companies focus on to help them forecast trends.

a) WEN RATEMAILS ....

b) POLARUP CUTRULE ....

c) ALCOHOLICGENT LENDSVETPOEM ....

d) SILLYFEET ....

e) ERECTHAIRCUT ....

⬜

Designing

Initial Ideas

1 Which of the following words could be used to describe good initial ideas? Tick the correct options.

A Detailed ☐   **B** Creative ☐

C Technical ☐   **D** Relevant ☐

E Random ☐   **F** Innovative ☐

G Focused ☐

2 Name two things that you should refer to when producing your initial ideas.

a) ....   **b)** ....

Exploring Ideas

3 **a)** List six elements that you should explore and experiment with at an early stage in the design process.

i) ....   **ii)** ....

iii) ....   **iv)** ....

v) ....   **vi)** ....

b) Briefly explain why it is important to experiment with different design elements at an early stage.

....

....

Colour

4 Fill in the missing words to complete the following sentences.

There is more to exploring colour than simply trying out different colour schemes. You can experiment

with different methods of .... colour. You can even try layering colour by combining

different ....

5 Give four different methods of applying colour to fabric.

a) ....   **b)** ....

c) ....   **d)** ....

Designing

Texture

1 Which of the following statements best describes **texture**? Tick the correct option.

    A A scale of different shades and tints of a colour

    B Contrasting areas of colour

    C A raised nap or pile

    D The tactile nature (feel) of a fabric or the appearance of having one

2 The statements below describe the different stages of the process of making a rubbing.
Number them **1–4** to show the correct order of events.

    A An impression of the texture will be left on the paper.

    B Use masking tape to hold the paper in place.

    C Rub the side of a wax crayon over the paper.

    D Place a piece of paper over a hard, textured surface, e.g. a piece of bark or a stone slab.

Proportion and Construction

3 Draw a line to match each term to the correct explanation.

Anthropometrics	The study of how people interact with objects around them.
Proportion	The relationship between different elements of a design in terms of size.
Ergonomics	To increase or decrease all measurements by the same ratio.
Scale	The study of average human measurements.

4 Below is a design for a bag.

60cm

a) What will the height of the bag be if you produce a 50% scale model? ....

b) What will the height of the bag be if you produce a $\frac{1}{4}$ scale model? ....

Designing

Fabrics

1 Choose the correct words from the options given to complete the following sentences.

design   **products**   **make**   **properties**   **combine**   **innovative**   **suitable**   **fabrics**

It is important to experiment with different fabrics to develop a better understanding of their

_____. This will allow you to select the most _____ fabric for the

job when you design different _____. It will also help you to _____

fabrics in an _____ way to create interesting products.

Surface Decoration and Embellishment

2 a) What is an **embellishment**? Tick the correct option.

A A functional feature or detail ☐   **B** A decorative feature or detail ☐

C An ergonomic feature or detail ☐   **D** An unnecessary design feature or detail ☐

b) Which of the following examples would be classed as embellishments? Tick the correct options.

A Beads ☐   **B** Press-studs ☐

C Overlocked stitching ☐   **D** Sequins ☐

E Ribbons ☐   **F** A zip ☐

G Interfacing ☐

Using ICT

3 a) What is ICT? Tick the correct option.

A Illustration and Colour Technology ☐

B Ideal Criteria for Textiles ☐

C Information Communication Technology ☐

D Important Computer Technology ☐

b) Suggest three ways in which ICT can be used when generating design ideas.

i) _____

ii) _____

iii) _____

Development

1 a) The statements below describe different stages of development in the design process. Number the stages **1–4** to show the correct order in which they should take place.

A Make modifications ◯

B Produce drawings of different views ◯

C Produce quick sketches ◯

D Develop more detailed drawings ◯

b) What is the purpose of the development process above? Tick the correct option.

A To make sure that you are happy with your initial ideas ◯

B To refine and improve your initial ideas ◯

C To prove that the designs are your own and have not been copied ◯

D To prove that you have good drawing skills ◯

c) Use your answers to part a) to answer the following questions. Write the correct number in the box provided.

i) At which stage of development should you start to think about the dimensions of your product and consider anthropometric data and ergonomics? ◯

ii) At which stage of development should you produce models? ◯

iii) At which stage of development should you make adjustments to details like necklines? ◯

iv) At which stage of development must you produce scale drawings? ◯

v) At which stage of development is it sufficient to just show outlines and key details? ◯

2 Which of the following statements best describes the term **modification**? Tick the correct option.

A Changing the overall design ◯

B Adjusting details of the design ◯

C Rejecting a particular design ◯

D Adding notes to a design drawing ◯

3 Fill in the missing word to complete the following sentence.

It is essential that you can _____ all your design decisions.

◯

Product Specification

Copyright of Designs

1 What is the purpose of copyright law? Tick the correct option.

A To ensure that products are of an acceptable quality. ◯

B To grant people the right to copy designs freely. ◯

C To ensure that products are safe for consumers to use. ◯

D To prevent people from copying a design without the owner's permission. ◯

The Product Specification

2 Fill in the missing words to complete the following sentence.

A product specification contains all the .... needed to produce a

.... of the product.

3 **a)** What should be included in a product specification? Tick the correct options.

A Rough sketches ◯ **B** Samples of materials ◯

C A mood board ◯ **D** A working drawing ◯

E Measurements ◯ **F** Desirable criteria ◯

G Aftercare information ◯ **H** Marketing material ◯

b) Name one other item that should be included in a product specification.

....

4 Circle the correct options in the sentences below.

A working drawing is a **colour / black and white** technical drawing. It shows the front and **back / aerial** views and includes **exploded / expanded** drawings where necessary. **Exact / Approximate** measurements need to be marked on the drawings along with details of **trends / seams**.

Industry Specifications

5 In industry, the product specification will incorporate specifications for different elements of the product. List three elements that will have their own detailed specification.

a) .... **b)** .... **c)** ....

Manufacturing Specification

The Manufacturing Specification

1 Which of the following statements about manufacturing specifications are true?
Tick the correct options.

A 'Manufacturing Specification' is the industry term for a 'Product Specification'. ⬭

B It is produced after a prototype has been made. ⬭

C It provides a detailed set of guidelines for the manufacturer to follow. ⬭

D It is produced after the first batch of products has been manufactured. ⬭

E It is used to produce a prototype of the product. ⬭

F It incorporates any final adjustments made to the prototype. ⬭

2 Choose the correct words from the options provided to complete the following sentences.

solutions   control   chart   quality   stage   equipment   flow   problems   critical   components

A manufacturing specification will include a list of materials and ...., a list of tools

and ...., a detailed work plan in the form of a ....

...., timings and guidelines for each separate .... of

manufacture and details of .... checks. It will identify the

.... points in the manufacturing process and possible ....

that may arise, along with ....

3 Below are various parts of a flow chart. Number them **1–8** to show the correct order in which they
should be joined together to create a general work plan (an actual flow chart would contain specific
details).

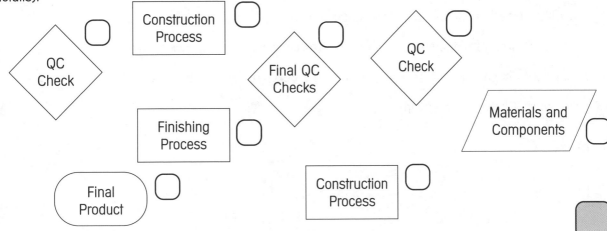

Fibres and Yarns

Fibres

1 (Circle) the correct options in the following sentences.

a) All fabrics are made from tiny hair-like structures called **yarns / fibres**.

b) **Short / Long** fibres are called staple fibres and **short / long** fibres are called filament fibres.

2 The table contains different categories of fibres.

Match the fibres **A–F** with the categories **1–3** in the table. Enter the appropriate number in the boxes provided.

A Silk ◯

B Acetate ◯

C Polyester ◯

D Polyethylene ◯

E Cashmere ◯

F Viscose ◯

Categories of Fibres	
1	Natural fibres
2	Synthetic fibres
3	Regenerated fibres

3 Briefly explain what a microfibre is.

Yarns

4 (Circle) the correct options in the following sentences.

a) Yarns are made by **matting / twisting** fibres together.

b) The worsted spinning system produces a **smooth / hairy** yarn.

c) The woollen spinning system produces a **smooth / hairy** yarn.

5 (Circle) the correct options in the following sentences.

a) In an S twist yarn, the fibres are spun in a(n) **clockwise / anticlockwise** direction.

b) In a Z twist yarn, the fibres are spun in a(n) **clockwise / anticlockwise** direction.

6 Name four different types of yarn.

a) ....

b) ....

c) ....

d) ....

Knitted Fabrics

1 Which of the following statements about knitted fabrics are true?
Cross out the incorrect statement in each pair.

a) Knitted fabrics are made from interlocking loops of yarn.
Knitted fabrics are made from interwoven threads of yarn.

b) Knitted fabrics lack elasticity.
Knitted fabrics are elastic.

c) Knitted fabrics are warm.
Knitted fabrics are cool.

2 What type of finishing process can be used to increase the warmth of knitted fabrics?
Tick the correct option.

A Napping ◯   **B** Weaving ◯

C Selvedge ◯   **D** Bonding ◯

3 Which of the following statements about weft knitted fabrics are true? Tick the correct options.

A They have vertical ribs. ◯

B Interlocking loops above and below each knitted row hold the fabric together. ◯

C They have O-shaped loops on the face. ◯

D The yarn is knitted in horizontal rows. ◯

E They include single and double jersey fabrics. ◯

F They are less elastic than warp knitted fabrics. ◯

Woven Fabrics

4 Which of the following statements about woven fabrics are true? Tick the correct options.

A They are made from two pieces of material bonded together. ◯

B They are strongest along the straight grain of the fabric. ◯

C They have V-shaped loops on the surface. ◯

D They fray easily when cut. ◯

E They are stronger and firmer the closer the weave is. ◯

F They are more elastic than knitted fabrics. ◯

◯

Fabrics

Types of Weave

1. The table contains the names of four types of weave.

   Match the statements **A–H** to the types of weave **1–4** in the table. Enter the appropriate number in the boxes provided.

	Types of Weave
1	Plain
2	Twill
3	Satin
4	Jacquard

   A Creates a diagonal pattern. ◯

   B The weft yarns pass over and under 4–7 warp yarns. ◯

   C Produces high quality fabrics that are very expensive. ◯

   D Examples include polyester, cotton, calico, muslin, taffeta and voile. ◯

   E Creates a smooth, shiny fabric. ◯

   F Examples include denim and gabardine. ◯

   G The simplest weave. ◯

   H Often used for high-end products like formal wear. ◯

Pile Fabrics

2. Which of the following statements best describes a pile fabric? Tick the correct option.

   A A knitted fabric with a brushed finish. ◯

   B A fabric with a diagonal bias. ◯

   C A fabric with a raised surface made from upright loops of yarn. ◯

   D A fabric made from layers of woven cloth bonded together. ◯

3. Which of the following fabrics are examples of pile fabrics? Tick the correct options.

   A Velvet ◯   **B** Denim ◯

   C Polyester ◯   **D** Terry towelling ◯

   E Damask ◯   **F** Corduroy ◯

4. Briefly explain what the term **nap** means.

   _____

   _____

   _____

Fabrics

Non-Woven Fabrics

1 Choose the correct words from the options given to complete the following sentences.

twisted   staples   chemicals   heat   water   stitching   raw

Non-woven fabrics are made from .... fibres rather than yarns. They are

constructed by using either .... to mat fibres the together, ...

to bond fibres together or .... to join layers of fibres together.

2 Which of the following statements about non-woven fabrics are true? Tick the correct options.

A They are strongest along the straight grain of the fabric. ◯

B They are not as strong or flexible as knitted and woven fabrics. ◯

C They do not fray easily when cut. ◯

D They have no elasticity. ◯

E The are non-permeable. ◯

Wool Felts, Needle Felts and Bonded Fabrics   Edexcel • OCR

3 The table contains the names of three types of non-woven fabric.

Match statements **A, B, C** and **D** to the types of non-woven fabric **1–3** in the table. Enter the appropriate number in the boxes provided.

A The fibres are glued together using a strong adhesive. ◯

B Fibres are dragged in different directions to interlock them. ◯

C Fibres are softened using a solvent so that they stick together. ◯

D A web of fibres is treated with a solution before being heated. ◯

	Non-Woven Fabrics
1	Wool felts
2	Needle felts
3	Bonded fabrics

4 a) Needle felts are made by passing the fibres through a series of…
Tick the correct option to complete the sentence.

A darning needles. ◯   **B** straight needles. ◯

C barbed needles. ◯   **D** knitting needles. ◯

b) Wool felts are finished by passing them through…
Tick the correct option to complete the sentence.

A mechanical rollers. ◯   **B** a drying machine. ◯

C a series of needles. ◯   **D** a water bath. ◯

Fabrics

1 Which type of fabric can be moulded and shaped into seamless clothing? Tick the correct option.

    A Lace ◯   **B** Rubber ◯   **C** Net ◯

    D Ceramic ◯   **E** Metal ◯

2 Which type of fabric is Tyvek? Tick the correct option.

    A Ceramic ◯   **B** Rubber ◯   **C** Paper ◯

    D Metal ◯   **E** Lace ◯

3 Which fabric is used in specialist garments made to withstand extreme conditions? Tick the correct option.

    A Ceramic ◯   **B** Net ◯   **C** Paper ◯

    D Metal ◯   **E** Lace ◯

4 Which type of fabric is manufactured on a net base? Tick the correct option.

    A Ceramic ◯   **B** Net ◯   **C** Paper ◯

    D Metal ◯   **E** Lace ◯

5 Circle the correct options in the following sentences.

Metal fibres like steel, copper and aluminium can be made into very **thin / thick** yarns and used in fabrics. They are used in electronic 'smart' fabrics because of their **insulating / conductive** properties.

6 Which type of textile products are made from glass fibres? Tick the correct option.

    A Swimwear ◯   **B** Architectural products ◯

    C Protective clothing ◯   **D** Curtains ◯

Choosing Fabrics

7 You are asked to design a form-fitting top for sprint runners. List three requirements that would affect your choice of fabric.

    a) ....

    b) ....

    c) ....

Fabrics

Properties of Fabrics

1 Which statement best describes what a **property** is? Tick the correct option.

A A method of construction ◯   **B** A quality or characteristic ◯

C A fabric's general appearance ◯   **D** The type of fibre a fabric is made from ◯

2 a) Fill in the missing word to complete the following sentence.

The properties of the fabric need to be matched to the _____ of the product.

b) What do designers use to help them carry out the process described in part a)? Tick the correct option.

A A trend forecasting agency ◯   **B** A mood board ◯

C A fabric chart ◯   **D** A Gantt chart ◯

Mixing Properties of Fabrics

3 The properties of a fabric can be enhanced by combining different fibres. What is this process called? Tick the correct option.

A Interlocking ◯   **B** Merging ◯

C Blending ◯   **D** Enhancing ◯

4 What is the resulting fabric called when you mix polyester with cotton? Tick the correct option.

A Cottonester ◯   **B** Polymix ◯

C Polycotton ◯   **D** Polymer cotton ◯

5 The table below shows some of the properties of polyester and wool.

Complete the table by writing down the properties you would expect to find in a polyester / wool blend based on this information.

Polyester	Polyester / Wool Blend	Wool
• Very strong • High elasticity • Low absorbency • Good crease resistance • Very durable • Not very warm		• Not very strong • High elasticity • High absorbency • Good crease resistance • Low durability • Very warm

Properties of Fibres and Fabrics

Properties of Fabrics

1 **a)** Which of the following fabrics are made from natural fibres? Tick the correct options.

A Polyester ⬭   **B** Elastane ⬭   **C** Linen ⬭

D Viscose ⬭   **E** Silk ⬭   **F** Acrylic ⬭

b) Which of the following fabrics are made from synthetic fibres? Tick the correct options.

A Polyester ⬭   **B** Elastane ⬭   **C** Linen ⬭

D Viscose ⬭   **E** Silk ⬭   **F** Acrylic ⬭

c) Which of the following fabric is made from regenerated fibres? Tick the correct option.

A Polyester ⬭   **B** Elastane ⬭   **C** Linen ⬭

D Viscose ⬭   **E** Silk ⬭   **F** Acrylic ⬭

2 Use the fabric chart on page 42 of your Essentials Revision Guide to answer the following questions.

a) Circle the correct option to answer the following questions.

i) Which of the following fabrics is the most absorbent?   **rayon / silk / nylon**

ii) Which of the following fabrics is the least flammable?   **wool / polyester / linen**

iii) Which of the following fabrics is the most elastic?   **elastane / wool / acrylic**

iv) Which of the following fabrics has the greatest strength and durability?   **acrylic / linen / acetate**

v) Which of the following fabrics is cool and absorbent?   **acrylic / nylon / polyester**

b) Identify a suitable fabric for each of the following specifications.

i) A fabric made from natural fibres that is strong, durable and elastic. ....

ii) A warm fabric with low absorbency. ....

iii) A fibre that can be blended with cotton to improve its elasticity and crease resistance.

....

3 Unscramble the letters to find four other factors that need to be considered when choosing a fabric.

a) INAUDIBLYALTER ....

b) COTFORM ....

c) BEITRAILWAY ....

d) STOC ....

Properties of Fibres and Fabrics

Special Properties

1 Choose the correct words from the options given to complete the following sentences.

built-in   **fabrics**   **textile**   **construction**   **properties**

To make them more useful to manufacturers, ... can have their

.... enhanced or have special properties .... Some

properties can be added to a .... product after ....

2 The table contains the names of three types of fibre that have special properties.

Match the descriptions of the properties **A**, **B** and **C** with the fibres **1–3** in the table. Enter the appropriate number in the boxes provided.

	Fibres
1	Elastane
2	Biodegradable fibres
3	Microfibres

A Has lots of extension. ⬭

B Small, fine fibres, up to 60 times finer than human hair. ⬭

C Produce lightweight, breathable fabrics. ⬭

3 Circle the correct options in the following sentences.

a) BioSteel is a very **strong / weak** fibre-based material.

b) Kevlar® is extremely **fragile / hardwearing**.

c) Gore-Tex® is an example of a fabric with a **breathable / airtight** membrane.

4 What is BioSteel made from? Tick the correct option.

A Casein from goats' milk and protein silk from spiders' webs ⬭

B Cellulose extracted from wood pulp ⬭

C The cocoon of a silk worm ⬭

D Chemicals derived from crude oil ⬭

5 What is the key property of Nomex®? Tick the correct option.

A Breathable ⬭

B Lightweight but extremely strong ⬭

C Water resistant ⬭

D Heat and flame resistant ⬭

Finishes

Applying Finishes

1 What are the three different categories of finishes?

a) .... **b)** .... **c)** ....

2 Give three good reasons for applying a finish to a fabric.

a) ....

b) ....

c) ....

3 Circle the correct options in the following sentences.

Finishes are applied at **the end / different stages** of the production process. They can **improve / reduce** the functionality of the product but **increase / reduce** its overall cost.

4 Which specifications should contain details of any finishes that need to be applied?
Tick the correct options.

A	Design specification	○	**B**	Product specification	○
C	Manufacturing specification	○	**D**	Component specification	○

Physical Finishes   Edexcel • OCR

5 The table contains the names of three physical finishes for fabrics.

a) Match the effects **A, B** and **C** with the finishes **1–3** in the table. Enter the appropriate number in the boxes provided.

A The fabric is left soft and fluffy. ○

B The fabric has a smooth finish. ○

C The resulting fabric consists of layers with different properties. ○

	Physical Finishes
1	Calendering
2	Laminating
3	Brushing

b) Match the example products **A, B** and **C** with the finishes **1–3** in the table. Enter the appropriate number in the boxes provided.

A Table cloths and aprons ○

B Chintz fabric and furnishings ○

C Bedding and fleeces ○

	Physical Finishes
1	Calendering
2	Laminating
3	Brushing

Biological Finishes

Edexcel

1 Choose the correct words from the options given to complete the following sentences.

polyester   brushes   pumice   rougher   softer   cellulose   cotton   celluloid

Biostoning uses a .... enzyme that acts on the fabric. It produces a 'worn' look and

a .... feel and can be applied to .... (especially denim) as

an alternative to rubbing with ....

2 a) Which type of finish involves an enzyme, which acts on the fabric to produce a sheen?
Tick the correct option.

A Biostoning ◯   **B** Biopolishing ◯

C Mercerising ◯   **D** Waterproofing ◯

b) Name two fabrics that the finish described in part a) can be applied to.

i) ....   **ii)** ....

Chemical Finishes

3 Which of the following processes are chemical finishes? Tick the correct options.

A Flameproofing ◯   **B** Waterproofing ◯

C Biopolishing ◯   **D** Mercerising ◯

E Biostoning ◯   **F** Calendering ◯

4 Are the following sentences about flameproof finishes true or false? Circle the correct option.

a) A water-repellent, silicon-based chemical is sprayed onto the fabric.   **TRUE / FALSE**

b) The fabric is placed in sodium hydroxide solution.   **TRUE / FALSE**

c) These finishes are applied to interior fabrics and furnishings.   **TRUE / FALSE**

d) They provide a protective layer that slows down the burning process.   **TRUE / FALSE**

e) They can be applied to cotton, linen and rayon.   **TRUE / FALSE**

5 What is the purpose of mercerising fabrics? Tick the correct option.

A To make the fabric water-repellent ◯

B To strengthen the fabric and make it more absorbent ◯

C To give the fabric a 'worn' look ◯

D To make the surface of the fabric softer and fluffier ◯

Finishes

Chemical Finishes (Cont.)

1 a) Which type of finish involves a resin- or chlorine-based chemical treatment?
Tick the correct option.

A Shrink resistance ◯

B Anti-static ◯

C Crease resistance ◯

D Anti-felting ◯

b) Name a fabric that the finish described in part a) can be applied to. ....

2 Circle the correct options in the following sentences.

Anti-felting finishes are applied to **cotton / woollen / synthetic** fabrics. They involve an **enzyme / resin / oxidative** treatment being applied to the **fabric / fleece / yarn**, which **dissolves / softens / strengthens** rough fibres. They prevent matting and felting whilst **retaining / increasing / decreasing** warmth.

3 Which of the following descriptions about anti-static finishes are true? Tick the correct options.

A They soften coarse fibres. ◯

B They stop the build up of electrostatic charge. ◯

C They are applied to products like underwear and carpets. ◯

D They take the form of a thin layer of resin on the surface of the fabric. ◯

E They stop the fabric from shrinking when machine washed. ◯

F They can be applied to synthetic fabrics. ◯

4 What two finishes would you apply to a woollen garment to increase its lifespan?

a) ....   b) ....

5 Would you ever apply both a mercerising finish and a water-repellent finish to the same fabric? Explain your answer.

....

....

6 Name two finishes that you would apply to an easy-care, white cotton shirt.

a) ....   b) ....

7 Name two finishes that you would apply to a fabric that was to be used for upholstering an armchair.

a) ....   b) ....

 Revision Guide Reference: Page 46

Other Finishes

AQA • OCR

1 Choose the correct words from the options given to complete the following sentences.

standards   applications   laws   properties   tested   labels   patterns

Some finishes have been developed for specialist .... Products cannot claim to

have the resulting .... on their .... unless they have been

fully .... against a set of ....

2 Which type of finish protects against general wear and tear? Tick the correct option.

A Ballistic resistance ⬭

B Fire resistance ⬭

C Spark resistance ⬭

D Abrasion resistance ⬭

3 Which of the following finishes are used on protective clothing for the emergency services?
Tick the correct options.

A Abrasion resistance ⬭   **B** Biostoning ⬭

C Fire resistance ⬭   **D** Spark resistance ⬭

E Ballistic resistance ⬭   **F** Mercerising ⬭

4 Which of the following finishes are used on body armour? Tick the correct options.

A Abrasion resistance ⬭   **B** Biostoning ⬭

C Fire resistance ⬭   **D** Spark resistance ⬭

E Ballistic resistance ⬭   **F** Mercerising ⬭

5 What type of finish would you apply to some overalls designed for a welder in the steel industry?

....

6 Name two finishes you might apply to the uniform worn by people who take part in the sport of fencing.

a) ....

b) ....

Components

Components

1. Choose the correct words from the options given to complete the following sentence.

   tear   functionality   stretch   enhance

   When creating a textiles product, various components can be used with fabric to

   _____ or embellish it, or add _____ .

2. The table below contains the names of four components used to add colour.

   Match descriptions **A, B, C** and **D** with the components **1–4** in the table. Enter the appropriate number in the boxes provided.

   A Specialist versions can be used to create 3D or glow-in-the dark designs. ◯

   B Used to cover large areas of fabric or yarn in solid colour. ◯

   C Can be used to 'stitch' designs onto the fabric. ◯

   D Can be used to 'draw' designs onto the fabric. ◯

	Components
1	Dyes
2	Inks
3	Paints
4	Embroidery threads

3. The table below contains the names of some more components.

   Match descriptions **A, B, C, D** and **E** with the components **1–5** in the table. Enter the appropriate number in the boxes provided.

   A Can be constructed into fabrics, using special needles, by hand or machine. ◯

   B Used to create flexible openings, like waist bands. ◯

   C Allow openings on products to be opened and closed as necessary. ◯

   D A fusible material used to reinforce fabrics. ◯

   E Also described as 'narrow fabrics'. ◯

	Components
1	Elastics
2	Yarns
3	Bindings
4	Fastening
5	Interfacing

4. **a)** List six different types of fastening.

   i) _____   ii) _____   iii) _____

   iv) _____   v) _____   vi) _____

   b) Briefly explain why it is important to consider the end-user when choosing a fastening.

   _____

   _____

Smart Materials and Technical Textiles

Technical Textiles

1 Complete the following sentence.

Technical textiles are manufactured for…

....

....

2 List four industries that use technical textiles.

a) ....   **b)** ....

c) ....   **d)** ....

Traditional Textiles for Modern Living

3 Which traditional fabric has been enhanced using new technology to reduce pilling and water absorption? Tick the correct option.

A Calico ◯   **B** Tweed ◯

C Jacquard ◯   **D** Polycotton ◯

Smart Materials

4 Are the following statements about smart materials true or false? Circle the correct option.

a) Some respond to changes in temperature.	**TRUE / FALSE**
b) They are all made of plastic.	**TRUE / FALSE**
c) They can respond to external stimuli.	**TRUE / FALSE**
d) Some can be activated by internal or external power sources.	**TRUE / FALSE**
e) They are constructed from metal fibres.	**TRUE / FALSE**
f) They all contain microchips.	**TRUE / FALSE**

5 Fill in the missing words to complete the following sentences.

a) Photochromic materials respond to changes in .... by changing colour.

b) Thermochromic materials respond to changes in .... by changing colour.

6 Name two traditional processes that can be used to apply smart technology to textiles.

a) ....   **b)** ....

Smart Materials and Technical Textiles

Wearable Technology (Conductive Textiles) — Edexcel • OCR

1 Which of the following materials can be made into conductive fibres, which can be incorporated into textile products? Tick the correct options.

A Nickel ⬭ B Acrylic ⬭

C Aluminium ⬭ D Plastic ⬭

E Silver ⬭ F Rubber ⬭

2 What are the four methods by which conductive materials can be applied to textiles?

a) .... b) ....

c) .... d) ....

3 What are the three main components needed to create a conductive textiles product? Tick the correct options.

A Technical tweed ⬭ B Microcapsules ⬭

C Conductive fibres ⬭ D Photochromic dye ⬭

E A power source ⬭ F Controls ⬭

4 What is a soft interface?

....

....

Power Assisted Textiles — Edexcel

5 What are the three different types of power source commonly used in power assisted textiles? Tick the correct options.

A Flexible batteries ⬭ B Kinetic energy ⬭

C Wind turbines ⬭ D Mains electricity ⬭

E Solar panels ⬭ F Electrostatic charge ⬭

Communication Textiles — Edexcel

6 Name two types of communication device that can be incorporated into textiles products.

a) .... b) ....

Smart Materials and Technical Textiles

Medical Textiles Edexcel

1 What are the two main functions of medical textiles? Tick the correct options.

A Communication ◯

B To provide a power source ◯

C To act as a soft interface ◯

D To aid healing ◯

E Entertainment ◯

F To monitor health ◯

2 The table contains the names of two different components that can be incorporated into textiles for medical purposes.

Match descriptions **A**, **B**, **C** and **D** with the components **1–2** in the table. Enter the appropriate number in the boxes provided.

A Allow medical staff to monitor vital signs. ◯

B Release scents and / or drugs when friction or heat is applied. ◯

C Incorporated into bandages and dressings. ◯

D Incorporated into wearable products, like vests for comfort and ease of use. ◯

	Components
1	Microcapsules
2	Electronic sensors

Nanotechnology

3 Draw a line to connect each term with the correct definition.

Nanotube		A trade name for commercial nanomaterials
Nanoparticle		A structure made from nanoparticles, which can conduct heat and electricity
NanoGrain®		A microscopic particle with specific physical and chemical properties

4 List four properties that can be introduced or enhanced in textiles through the use of nanoparticles.

a) ....

b) ....

c) ....

d) ....

◯

Modelling Colour and Decoration

Modelling

1 Why is modelling an important part of design development?

2 Which of the following processes are examples of modelling? Tick the correct options.

A Producing the final product ⬭

B Producing small-test pieces ⬭

C Producing a design specification ⬭

D Producing small-scale versions of the end product ⬭

E Producing full-size prototypes ⬭

F Producing an evaluation ⬭

Printing

3 Draw a line to match each printing method to the correct description.

Block printing	Heated rollers are used to transfer a design from sublimation paper onto fabric.
Screen printing	A series of rollers transfer an engraved design onto fabric.
Engraved roller printing	A design is cut into wood, coated with pigment and then 'stamped' onto the fabric.
Heat transfer printing	Pigment is pushed through a frame-mounted screen using a specialist tool.

4 Match the statements **A-F** to the methods of printing **1-6** in the table. Write the appropriate number in the boxes provided.

	Methods of Printing
1	Digital printing
2	Heat transfer printing
3	Engraved roller printing
4	Stencilling
5	Screen printing
6	Block printing

A The pigment is applied to the fabric through holes cut in cardboard. ⬭

B Only suitable for fabrics that contain more than 50% synthetic fibres. ⬭

C Uses a device called a squeegee. ⬭

D Allows you to create complex designs quickly and easily. ⬭

E A separate roller is required for each different colour. ⬭

F The design is created in relief. ⬭

Modelling Colour and Decoration

Dyeing and Industrial Practices

5 Are the following statements about dyeing true or false? Circle the correct option.

a) Stronger colours can be achieved with natural fibres. **TRUE / FALSE**

b) The fibre content of fabrics does not affect the resulting colour. **TRUE / FALSE**

c) There are different types of synthetic and natural dyes available. **TRUE / FALSE**

d) Some dyes require fixatives or binding agents. **TRUE / FALSE**

e) All dyes are naturally occurring. **TRUE / FALSE**

f) The same results are achieved regardless of the stage at which dyeing takes place. **TRUE / FALSE**

6 Which of the following dyeing methods are suitable for use in the classroom.
Tick the correct options.

A Pigment dyeing ⬜   **B** Disperse dyeing ⬜   **C** Garment dyeing ⬜

D Vegetable dyeing ⬜   **E** Direct dyeing ⬜

7 Draw a line to match each word to the correct definition.

Sublimation	A full-size, working model of a product.
Pigment	A colour-carrying substance.
Bespoke	Standing out from the background.
Mordant	An agent used to 'fix' the colour produced by a natural dye.
Relief	The paper on which designs are created for transfer printing.
Prototype	A unique, one-off product.

8 Answer the following questions by writing **direct** or **disperse** to show which type of dyeing process is being described.

a) This process does not require a fixative. ....

b) Used for synthetic fibres like polyester, nylon and acrylic. ....

c) This process can only be carried out once. ....

d) The dye is applied under pressure. ....

e) Only a single colour can be applied to the fabric. ....

Modelling Colour and Decoration

Resist Methods of Dyeing — Edexcel • OCR

1 Fill in the missing words to complete the following sentence.

Resist methods of dyeing _____ the dye from _____ areas of the fabric to produce a pattern.

2 Which of the following items can be used to 'resist' dye? Tick the correct options.

A String ◯   B Wax ◯

C Salt ◯   D Flour ◯

E Metallic oxides ◯   F Rice paste ◯

Garment Dyeing — OCR

3 a) At what stage of production does garment dyeing take place? Tick the correct option.

A The yarn is dyed before the fabric is made. ◯

B The fabric is dyed before production starts. ◯

C The cut fabric pattern pieces are dyed. ◯

D The product is dyed after construction. ◯

b) Which type of fibres or yarns is garment dyeing suitable for? Tick the correct option.

A Natural fibres or blends ◯   B Synthetic fibres ◯

C Regenerated fibres ◯   D Blends only ◯

Surface Decoration

4 The table contains the names of three different methods of surface decoration.

Match descriptions **A**, **B**, and **C** with the methods of surface decoration **1–3** in the table. Enter the appropriate number in the boxes provided.

A Adding decorative components such as beads, shells and mirrors. ◯

B Fabric shapes stitched to a background fabric. ◯

C Textiles constructed from smaller samples of fabric joined together. ◯

	Surface Decoration
1	Appliqué
2	Patchwork
3	Embellishment

Surface Decoration (Cont.)

5 What is shisha work? ....

....

6 The tables contains four different methods for adding surface decoration to fabrics.

Match descriptions **A–F** to methods of decoration **1–4** in the table. Enter the appropriate number in the boxes provided.

A Created from a wide range of decorative stitches. ◯

B Add texture and colour by creating a raised design. ◯

C A fine zig-zag or straight stitch is used to attach fabric shapes. ◯

D The design can be printed onto special paper using a standard printer. ◯

E The shapes can be strengthened using interfacing. ◯

F Glow-in-the-dark paper can be used to create special effects. ◯

	Method
1	Transfers
2	Embroidery
3	3D Paints
4	Appliqué

7 **a)** Which type of dyes are used for transfer printing techniques? Tick the correct option.

A Direct dyes ◯ **B** Sublimation dyes ◯

C Disperse dyes ◯ **D** Resist dyes ◯

b) What three forms do the dyes described in part a) come in?

i) ....

ii) ....

iii) ....

8 What is used to apply transfers to fabric? Tick the correct option.

A Scanner ◯ **B** Digital camera ◯

C Heat press / iron ◯ **D** Hand stitching ◯

◯

Modelling Fabrics

Fabrics

1 a) Fill in the missing words to complete the following sentence.

Designers must choose fabrics that have .... suitable for the

.... of the end product.

b) Briefly explain how modelling helps designers to fulfil the statement in part a).

....

....

....

Manipulation
Edexcel • OCR

2 Are the following statements about fabric manipulation true or false? Circle the correct option.

a) Manipulation is another term for adding colour to fabric. **TRUE / FALSE**

b) Manipulation changes the shape, structure or texture of a fabric. **TRUE / FALSE**

c) Manipulation can involve physical and / or chemical processes. **TRUE / FALSE**

d) Manipulation includes basic construction techniques like cutting and hemming. **TRUE / FALSE**

e) Manipulation techniques include felting fibres, moulding fabrics and Shibori. **TRUE / FALSE**

3 What is put between layers of fabric to create texture when quilting? Tick the correct option.

A Cardboard ☐   **B** Interfacing ☐

C Binding ☐   **D** Wadding ☐

4 a) Which type of properties are an advantage in fabrics to be used for moulding and Shibori? Tick the correct option.

A Elastic ☐   **B** Thermoplastic ☐

C Abrasive ☐   **D** Chemical malleability ☐

b) Which of the following statements best explains the type of properties discussed in part a)? Tick the correct option.

A The fabric returns to its original shape as soon as the force is removed. ☐

B The fabric's shape can be changed permanently when pressure is applied. ☐

C When heat is applied, the fabric holds its new shape until heated again. ☐

D The fabric holds its original shape in all conditions. ☐

Modelling with ICT

1 Which of the following statements describe advantages of using ICT for modelling?
Tick the correct options.

A Buying the appropriate hardware and software can be very expensive. ◯

B It allows you to evaluate designs without spending money on materials and components. ◯

C It requires specialist skills and knowledge to operate the software effectively. ◯

D You can make modifications quickly and easily without starting from scratch each time. ◯

E A computer representation cannot accurately communicate qualities like 'movement' and 'feel'. ◯

2 Choose the correct words from the options provided to complete the following sentences.

2D   mapping   pattern   colourways   3D   scale   importing

a) ICT can be used to create a repeat _____ and adjust the

_____ to suit the product.

b) You can experiment with different _____ for your design quickly and easily using ICT.

c) You can use image _____ to create a _____ representation of

what your end product will look like.

Spreadsheets

3 What can spreadsheets be used for during design development? Tick the correct options.

A Producing drawings ◯   **B** Calculating production costs ◯

C Making a prototype ◯   **D** Writing detailed notes ◯

E Cost comparisons ◯   **F** Recording test data ◯

Digital Cameras and Scanners

4 a) Suggest one way in which a digital camera can be used during design development.

_____

b) Suggest one way in which a scanner can be used during design development.

_____

◻

Pattern Making

Pattern Making

1 The table contains different methods of creating patterns.

Match descriptions **A, B, C** and **D** with the methods **1–4** in the table. Enter the appropriate number in the boxes provided.

A Trace around standard 2D shapes and then modify. ◯

B Buy a pre-made pattern and cut to size. ◯

C Take apart an existing product and use the pieces to create a pattern. ◯

D Input parameters and measurements. ◯

	Methods
1	Disassembly
2	Commercial patterns
3	Standard pattern blocks
4	Pattern generation software

2 The following statements describe different stages of pattern making and modification. Number them **1–4** to show the correct order of events.

A Adjust the fit using a mannequin or live model. ◯

B Modify and refine the paper pattern. ◯

C Produce a pattern for your product. ◯

D Use the pattern to make a toile. ◯

3 Which organisation regulates the standard sizes for garments? Tick the correct option.

A FSI ◯   **B** FairTrade ◯

C BSI ◯   **D** IFAT ◯

4 What does this pattern marking mean?

Lay Planning

5 Which of the following factors need to be considered when lay planning? Tick the correct options.

A How to minimise wastage ◯   **B** The colour of the fabric ◯

C The nap of the fabric ◯   **D** The fibre content ◯

E Pattern alignment ◯   **F** Avoiding the selvedge ◯

Toiles

1 Choose the correct words from the options given to complete the following sentences.

products   lightweight   prototype   modelling   modifications   calico

A toile is the name given to a .... garment. It is usually made from

.... cotton, such as ...., or another cheap fabric. The term

'toile' is commonly used to describe the .... or prototyping of all textile

.... In industry, several toiles may be made for a single product as

.... are made to the design.

2 Are the following statements about toiles true or false? Circle the correct option.

a) Toiles are always full-size representations of the end product.   **TRUE / FALSE**

b) A toile can be used to evaluate a design before making the final product.   **TRUE / FALSE**

c) Making a toile allows you to identify where modifications are needed.   **TRUE / FALSE**

d) Toiles are often made from silk because it is lightweight.   **TRUE / FALSE**

e) Making a toile can help you evaluate production methods and estimate costs.   **TRUE / FALSE**

3 Give three advantages of producing small-scale models of your product.

a) ....

b) ....

c) ....

Industrial Practices

4 The following statements describe the various stages of product development used in industry.
Number the stages **1–8** to show the correct order of events.

A A design is produced. ◯

B The final product is manufactured. ◯

C A product specification is put together. ◯

D The client provides a brief. ◯

E The manufacturing specification is created. ◯

F A sample garment is made. ◯

G A design specification is put together. ◯

H A toile is made. ◯

Construction Techniques

1 **a)** The table contains diagrams of four different temporary methods of construction.

Match the names of the methods **A, B, C** and **D** to the diagrams **1–4** in the table. Write the appropriate number in the boxes provided.

A Basting ◯   **B** Tailor's tacking ◯

C Tacking ◯   **D** Pinning ◯

b) What is tacking used for?

....

....

c) What is tailor's tacking used for?

....

	Method
1	
2	
3	
4	

Machine Stitching

2 The table contains the names of five different types of machine stitches.

Match descriptions **A, B, C, D** and **E** with the types of machine stitches **1–5** in the table. Enter the appropriate number in the boxes provided.

A A combination of several stitches used for neatening the edge of a seam or garment. ◯

B Used for stitching jersey (knitted) fabrics. ◯

C A basic neatening stitch. ◯

D A basic stitch that is sometimes referred to as lockstitch. ◯

E Used for either finishing a seam or stitching jersey (knitted) fabrics together. ◯

	Machine Stitches
1	Straight Stitch
2	Zigzag (single step zigzag)
3	Zigzag (double step zigzag)
4	Chainstitch
5	Overlock

3 What is used to weld fabrics together? Tick the correct option.

A An adhesive web ◯   **B** A chemical solution ◯

C Heat or radio waves ◯   **D** An overlocker ◯

Construction Techniques

Types of Seam

1 The diagrams below show two types of seam.

A

B

a) What is the name of seam A? ....

b) What type of clothing is seam A used for?

....

c) What is the name of seam B? ....

d) What type of clothing is seam B used for?

....

2 Fill in the missing words to complete the following sentences.

An .... seam is standard on many textile products made in industry. It requires a

special machine, which trims and .... the edge whilst ....

This type of seam can be used inside a garment for .... or on the outside to add

....

Seam Finishes

3 What is the purpose of seam finishes? Tick the correct options.

A To permanently join two pieces of fabric

B To give a neat, finished appearance

C To temporarily hold fabric in place during construction

D To provide decoration

E To prevent fraying

F To make the seam watertight

Quality Control

Quality Assurance and Quality Control

1 Draw a line to match each term to the correct definition.

| Quality assurance | | A system put in place to ensure that the end product is well made and fit for purpose. |

| Quality control | | A guarantee that the product is well made and fit for purpose. |

2 List the three main stages where quality control should take place.

a) ....   b) ....

c) ....

Evaluating Designs

3 Choose the correct words from the options given to complete the following sentences.

target   manufacturing   purpose   nothing   design   criteria   market   safe

It is important to test and evaluate your designs continuously to ensure they meet all the essential

.... on your .... specification and that the end product will

be fit for ...., suitable for the ....,

well made and .... to use.

4 Which of the following words best describe the type of tests you should carry out on materials?
Tick the correct options.

A Random ⬭   **B** Fair ⬭   **C** Controlled ⬭

D General ⬭   **E** Relevant ⬭   **F** Specific ⬭

Identifying Quality Control Checks

5 For each of the following processes, suggest an appropriate quality control check.

a) Hemming a skirt. ....

b) Attaching buttons to the front of a shirt. ....

c) Creating button holes on the front of a shirt. ....

Technical Tests
Edexcel • AQA

1 The table contains properties that can be tested for in textiles.

Match the descriptions of tests **A, B, C** and **D** with the properties **1–4** in the table. Enter the appropriate number in the boxes provided.

A Rub with a sandpaper block until a hole appears. ◯

B Measure how much extension occurs when a force is applied. ◯

C Measure whether the fabric slows down the transfer of heat from boiling water to the surroundings. ◯

D Observe how a sample of fabric burns when set alight. ◯

	Properties
1	Elasticity
2	Abrasion
3	Flammability
4	Insulation

2 a) Fill in the missing words to complete the following description of a test for crease resistance.

Cut 3 equal .... of fabric. Crumple each piece in your .... for

10, 20, and 30 .... Observe how the fabric .... when it is

released after each test.

b) What device could you use to record the test described in part a)?

....

3 a) Which fabrics smell like burning paper and turn into a grey powder when set alight?
Tick the correct options.

A Viscose ◯   **B** Cotton ◯

C Polyester ◯   **D** Acrylic ◯

E Elastane ◯

b) Which fabrics burn quickly, shrink, melt and drip when set alight?
Tick the correct options.

A Viscose ◯   **B** Cotton ◯

C Polyester ◯   **D** Acrylic ◯

E Elastane ◯

◯

Regulations and Standards

Regulations

1 Choose the correct words from the options given to complete the following sentences.

Parliament   voluntary   manufacturing   practice   designers   compulsory   regulatory

There are many .... bodies that look after consumer interests. Many of these are

set up by .... groups to provide a .... code of

.... for their members. These groups provide guidance to ....

and manufacturers. Other regulations are governed by Acts of .... and are

....

Standards and Safety Standards

2 What is a **standard**? Tick the correct option.

    A   The most common way of carrying out a process ☐

    B   A law controlling a specific area of manufacture ☐

    C   An award for producing a high quality product ☐

    D   A set of precise criteria that ensure a certain level of safety or quality ☐

3 Who is responsible for regulating standards in the UK? ....

4 a) In the box, produce a sketch of the BSI Kitemark.

b) What does the BSI Kitemark assure consumers of? Tick the correct option.

    A   The product is ethically produced ☐

    B   The product has been made in the UK ☐

    C   The product has been tested against recognised standards ☐

    D   The product is used by the royal household ☐

c) Which other symbol offers similar assurance to the BSI Kitemark? Tick the correct option.

    A   The Fairtrade label ☐   **B**   The CE symbol ☐

    C   A Royal Warrant of Appointment ☐   **D**   The Country of Origin label ☐

Regulations and Standards

Safety of Children's Products

1 There are certain factors that must be considered when designing children's products, which are not as important when designing products for adults.

Give two factors that are essential for children's products.

a) ....

b) ....

2 Are the following statements about children's products true or false? Circle the correct option.

a) They must be able to withstand extreme temperatures.   **TRUE / FALSE**

b) They must not have stuffing or wadding that could be pulled out and cause
a choking hazard.   **TRUE / FALSE**

c) They must not be made from materials or fabric that could melt or catch fire. **TRUE / FALSE**

d) They must have visible fastenings.   **TRUE / FALSE**

e) Dyes, paint and inks must not contain any harmful substances.   **TRUE / FALSE**

Legislation   AQA

3 a) What is the meaning of the Food Imitation Regulations, 1989? Tick the correct options.

   A   Components on children's products must not resemble food. ◯

   B   Children's products must not resemble food. ◯

   C   Components on children's products must resemble food. ◯

   D   Children's products must resemble food. ◯

b) Give one other regulation that applies to children's products.

....

Safety of Other Products

4 For each of the following products, give one important health and safety consideration.

a) An oven glove.

....

b) A pair of shoes for people over 65 years of age.

....

Health and Safety

Health and Safety in the Classroom

1 a) Choose the correct 'p' word from the options given to complete the following sentences.

procedures   processes   prevent   practical   potential   protective   plan

When working on a _____ project in the classroom, you need to make a list of all

the equipment and _____ you will need to use and then identify the

_____ hazards of using them. To reduce the associated risks and

_____ injury, you must put a _____ in place that includes safety

_____ and details of the _____ clothing that must be worn.

b) What is the process described in part a) called? Tick the correct option.

A Hazard identification ⬭   **B** Safety assurance ⬭

C Risk assessment ⬭   **D** Injury prevention ⬭

Health and Safety in the Workplace

2 a) Who is responsible for ensuring the physical safety of employees in the workplace?
Tick the correct option.

A Factory Foreman ⬭   **B** Health and Safety Officer ⬭

C Human Resources Manager ⬭   **D** First Aid Official ⬭

b) List three ways in which the person in part a) can ensure employee safety.

i) _____

ii) _____

iii) _____

3 The Control of Substances Hazardous to Health Regulations, 2002, protects employees from the dangers
of substances used in the workplace. They are also referred to as…
Tick the correct option to complete the sentence.

A CSHH. ⬭   **B** CSHR. ⬭

C COSH. ⬭   **D** COSHH. ⬭

Potential Hazards

1 For each of the processes below, identify one safety guideline that should be followed.

a) Fusing

....

b) Spreading and cutting

....

c) Stain removal

....

d) Moving around the general working area

....

2 The table contains examples of processes that are potential safety hazards.

Match safety guidelines **A, B, C** and **D** with the processes **1–4** in the table. Enter the appropriate number in the boxes provided.

A Keep fingers away from the needles during operation. ◯

B Only turn the steam function on when ready to use steam. ◯

C Only use solvents in a well-ventilated room. ◯

D Keep walkways clear. ◯

	Process
1	Organising your work area
2	Stain removal
3	Pressing
4	Sewing

3 Which items of protective clothing are essential when working with dyes? Tick the correct options.

A Rubber boots ◯   **B** Hard hat ◯

C Hair net ◯   **D** Gloves ◯

E Apron ◯   **F** High visibility vest ◯

4 Give two safety guidelines that apply to all electrical equipment.

a) ....

b) ....

Planning Production

Manufacturing Specification

1 What does a manufacturing specification need to include? Tick the correct options.

A Optional extras for the manufacturer's consideration ⬜

B A plan with timings for each stage of manufacture ⬜

C Instructions with working drawings ⬜

D A time plan ⬜

E Rough sketches of the end product ⬜

F Details of quality control checks ⬜

Gantt Charts, Time Plans and Quality Control Checks

2 Choose the correct words from the options given to complete the following sentences.

time   garments   manufacturing   order   money   stages   timeline   cost   modelling   type

A Gantt chart shows the overall .... for the .... process. The

process is broken down into separate ...., showing the correct

.... of work and the amount of .... allocated for each stage.

3 What costs will a Production Manager calculate from a time plan? Tick the correct options.

A Cost of advertising ⬜   **B** Cost of making at each phase ⬜

C Cost of distribution ⬜   **D** Overall manufacture cost of product ⬜

E Cost of finishing ⬜   **F** Cost to consumer (i.e. Retail Price) ⬜

4 What four key pieces of information should be included in the manufacturing specification for each quality control check that needs to be carried out?

a) ....   **b)** ....

c) ....   **d)** ....

5 What is a tolerance? Tick the correct option.

A An exact measurement ⬜

B A range of acceptable measurements ⬜

C The amount of additional fabric needed for hems and seams ⬜

D A raw, unfinished edge on a piece of fabric ⬜

Systems and Control   Edexcel • OCR

1 **a)** In the manufacturing process, what are **systems**? Tick the correct option.

   A   The software used to operate the machinery ⬭

   B   The various teams within the workforce ⬭

   C   Regulated processes and procedures ⬭

   D   Machines used for manufacture ⬭

   b)   What is the main purpose of systems?

_____

2 How can control systems be represented within a manufacturing specification? Tick the correct option.

   A   In a graph ⬭   **B**   In a Gantt chart ⬭

   C   In a flow chart ⬭   **D**   In a star profile ⬭

3 The table contains three control areas.

Match descriptions **A**, **B** and **C** with the control areas **1–3** in the table. Enter the appropriate number in the boxes provided.

   A   The end results, e.g. a finished product or an approved design / prototype. ⬭

   B   The starting point, e.g. materials and components or a brief from the client. ⬭

   C   These bring about change, e.g. cutting and assembly or feedback from the client. ⬭

	Control Areas
1	Inputs
2	Transformation processsess
3	Outputs

4 Choose the correct words from the options given to complete the following sentences.

     system   **manufacturing**   **faults**   **stage**   **corrected**   **built-in**

Feedback is a _____ method of correcting problems (usually with quality) that occur

within a _____ . At several points during the _____ process,

checks are carried out on the product. If these reveal _____ the product is referred

back to the appropriate _____ to have the fault _____ .

⬭

Planning Production

1 a) Draw arrows on this factory plan to show the movement of the product from one area to another.

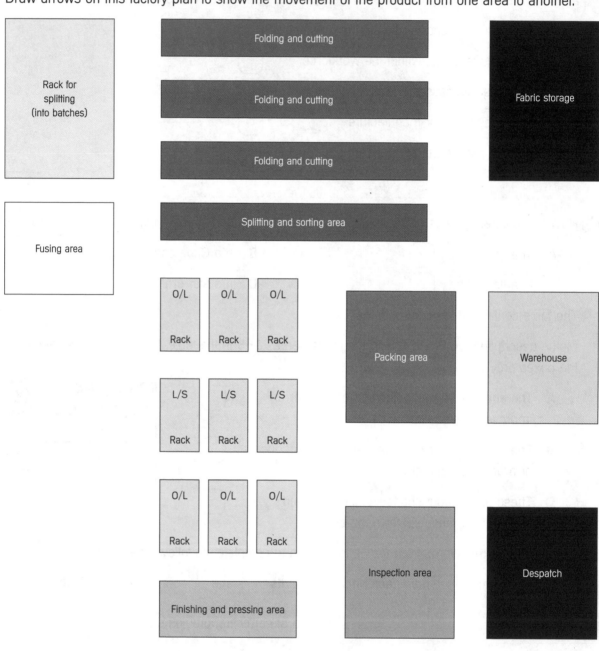

b) Name three areas on the factory plan above where you would expect quality control checks to take place.

i) ....

ii) ....

iii) ....

Computers in the Textiles Industry

Computer Systems

1 List three key advantages of using computers in business.

a) ....

b) ....

c) ....

2 What do the following abbreviations stand for?

a) CIM ....

b) CAA ....

c) CAD ....

d) CAM ....

3 What is CAM? Tick the correct option.

A Computers are used at every stage of planning, design and manufacture. ☐

B Computers are used in areas such as cutting, sewing and pressing. ☐

C Computers are used in areas such as marketing, sales and stock control. ☐

D Computers are used in design development and pattern making. ☐

4 What does EPOS stand for? Tick the correct option.

A Electronic Purchase of Sale ☐   **B** Electric Protective Skype ☐

C Electronic Point of Sale ☐   **D** Electronic Pattern Original Software ☐

New Technology

5 What is 'virtual imaging'? Tick the correct option.

A Rough sketches of an initial design idea ☐

B A working drawing produced on a computer ☐

C A computer representation of a product ☐

D An image streamed during video conferencing ☐

Computers in the Textiles Industry

New Technology (Cont.)

6 Unscramble the letters to find four other types of new technology being used in business.

a) GLIBGONG ....

b) PESKY ....

c) TINANTS NAMESGIGS ....

d) COILAS TENGROWINK ISSET ....

Examples of How ICT is Used

7 The table contains processes that involve the use of ICT in the textiles industry.

Match the ICT systems **A**, **B**, **C** and **D** with the processes **1–4** in the table. Enter the appropriate number in the boxes provided.

	Process
1	Design
2	Manufacture
3	Distribution
4	Sales

A EPOS and PDM software ◯

B Input digital images via a camera or scanner ◯

C Computerised lay planning and cutting tables ◯

D RFID Tagging ◯

8 a) At what stage is EDI (Electronic Data Interchange) normally used? Tick the correct option.

A Design ◯   **B** Manufacture ◯

C Distribution ◯   **D** Sales and marketing ◯

b) At what stage is 3D body scanning often used? Tick the correct option.

A Design ◯   **B** Manufacture ◯

C Distribution ◯   **D** Sales and marketing ◯

9 Choose the correct words from the options given to complete the following sentences.

processing   promote   spreadsheet   security   websites   advertising

a) You can use ICT to .... a product via .... in the form of

on-line .... or e-tailing.

b) At the sales stage, ICT can also be used for .... tagging.

c) Word .... software and .... software are used for ◯

everyday work and communication.

Computers in the Textiles Industry

The Three Phases

1 Below are the three main phases in the creation of commercial textiles. Number them **1–3** to show the order in which they take place.

A Post-production ◯

B Pre-production ◯

C Production ◯

2 Choose the correct words from the options given to complete the following sentences.

Internet   graphics   mood   design

In the design phase, you can research _____ ideas using the

_____ . You can then present ideas using _____ boards developed

using specialised _____ packages.

3 The table contains the three main phases in the creation of commercial textiles.

Match descriptions **A, B** and **C** with the phases **1–3** in the table. Enter the appropriate number in the boxes provided.

A A web launch and virtual fashion show can be used to promote a new product. ◯

B A 3D Image Draping system can be used to help visualise the product. ◯

C Software is used to record data during the testing of materials and components. ◯

	Phases
1	Pre-production
2	Production
3	Post-production

4 During which manufacturing phase is the product sent to a retail outlet, where it can be tracked using a computerised bar code system called EPOS? Tick the correct option.

A Pre-production phase ◯

B Production phase ◯

C Post-production phase ◯

5 During which manufacturing phase can a 3D representation of a garment be generated by mapping a flat 2D pattern onto a computer model called an 'Avatar'? Tick the correct option.

A Pre-production phase ◯

B Production phase ◯

C Post-production phase ◯

Industrial Clothing Manufacture

Production Systems

1 The table contains the four main types of production system.

Match descriptions **A, B, C** and **D** with the production systems **1–4** in the table. Enter the appropriate number in the boxes provided.

A A reasonable number of products are produced, possibly to meet seasonal demand. `2`

B The product is made by one individual (or a very small team) using traditional methods of manufacture. `1`

	Production Systems
1	Individual or job production
2	Batch production
3	Mass or volume production
4	Haute Couture

C An exclusive, one-off product is produced by a highly skilled individual or small team using the highest quality materials available. `4`

D A large number of identical products are manufactured continuously over a long period of time. `3`

2 What is repetitive flow production? Tick the correct option.

A The production of high volume items, where the process runs 24 hours a day and never shuts down.

B Each operator performs a single task repeatedly, passing the work 'along the production line'.

C Manufacture is divided into sub-assembly lines that concentrate on one area of the process.

D The product is made from start to finish by a small team, who begin work on the next product as soon as it is finished.

3 Which term used to describe garments made in large quantities and standard sizes? Tick the correct option.

A Off-the-peg ⬭   **B** Bespoke ⬭

C Designer ⬭   **D** Just-in-time ⬭

4 Fill in the missing word to complete the following sentence.

Straight line production can also be referred to as _____ production.

Production Systems (Cont.)

5 Draw lines to connect each production system to the correct product.

Batch production		An expensive and exclusive designer evening gown from a Paris fashion house.
Haute Couture		A limited edition bridal gown only sold by a handful of retailers.
Mass production		Canvas beach shoes sold in department stores from February to August.
Job production		A basic white t-shirt sold at a low price by large supermarkets all over the country.

6 a) Which type of system is being described below? Tick the correct option.

This form of management requires materials, components and sub-assemblies to arrive from suppliers and other manufacturers a short period before they are needed.

A On demand distribution ◯   **B** Just-in-time stock management ◯

C Batch production ◯   **D** Mass production ◯

b) Give two advantages of the system described in part a).

i) ....

ii) ....

c) Give one disadvantage of the system described in part a).

....

7 List four factors that need to be considered when deciding what type of production system to use.

a) ....

b) ....

c) ....

d) ....

Advertising and Marketing

Advertising

1 List four different media used for advertising.

a) ....

b) ....

c) ....

d) ....

2 Fill in the missing words to complete the three different examples of advertising used in stores.

a) Point-of-.. material

b) Swing ....

c) Window ....

3 The British Code of Advertising is an example of a piece of legislation that was put in place to protect the public from misleading adverts. Give one more example.

....

Marketing

4 What is **marketing**? Tick the correct option.

A Advertising a product ◯

B Selling a product ◯

C Promoting a product ◯

D All of these things ◯

E-Commerce

5 Briefly explain what **e-commerce** is.

....

6 Are the following statements about e-commerce true of false? Circle the correct option.

a) Consumers who make an electronic purchase from a European retailer have the same rights as they would had they purchased the product in-store in the UK. **TRUE / FALSE**

b) E-commerce includes transactions made by mail-order and in specialist shops. **TRUE / FALSE**

c) 'E-tailing' and 'Internet Shopping' are alternative names for e-commerce. **TRUE / FALSE**

Packaging

1 Write **primary** or **secondary** alongside each of the following items to indicate what type of packaging they are.

a) Cellophane wrappers

b) Bottles

c) Shrink wrap

d) Corrugated cardboard box

e) Pallets

f) Colourful card box

2 Briefly explain the difference between primary and secondary packaging.

3 What type of packaging requires designer input and may even have its own design specification?

4 Choose the correct words from the options given to complete the following sentences.

try   protection   target   visible   product

When a designer starts to generate ideas for a piece of packaging, they need to consider what the

_____ is, how much _____ is needed and who the

_____ market is. They also need to think about whether the actual product needs to

be _____ to the consumer and whether the consumer needs to be able to

_____ or test the product.

5 Circle the correct options to complete the sentences below.

Most packaging is **kept / discarded** after purchase. This generates **small / large** amounts of **energy / waste**. When **designing / manufacturing** packaging, it is important to consider how its impact on the environment can be **reduced / increased**.

Labelling

1 The table contains some of the types of information found on a label.

Match the descriptions **A** to **F** with the types of information **1–6** in the table. Enter the appropriate number in the boxes provided.

A A code of lines and numbers that provides information about the product. ◯

B Information that communicates the 'values' of the product and may influence consumer choice. ◯

C Essential warnings, e.g. keep away from fire. ◯

D International symbols that tell the consumer how best to care for the product. ◯

E Information regarding the type, size and style of product. ◯

F Numbers that relate to the standards which the product has been tested for. ◯

	Information
1	Product details
2	Barcode
3	Care labels
4	Safety advice
5	Standard number(s)
6	Ethical information

2 The table below contains four different wash care symbols.

Match the descriptions **A, B, C** and **D** to the aftercare symbols **1-4** in the table. Write the appropriate number in the boxes provided.

A Machine wash ◯

B Dry clean ◯

C Iron or press ◯

D Hand wash ◯

	Symbols
1	
2	
3	
4	

3 Name three different types of labels?

a) ....

b) ....

c) ....

◯

Consumer Protection   AQA • OCR

1 The table contains regulations for consumer protection.

Match descriptions **A, B, C** and **D** with the regulations **1-4** in the table. Enter the appropriate number in the boxes provided.

A It is illegal to sell products that do not match the minimum weight or quantity shown on the packaging.

B It is illegal to make false claims about a product.

C The fibre content of a fabric must be shown on the label.

D Products must correspond with their description, be of a satisfactory quality and be fit for their purpose.

	Regulations
1	The Trade Descriptions Act
2	The Sale Of Goods Act
3	The Weights And Measures Act
4	The Textiles Products (Indication of Fibre Content) Regulations

2 Which of the following rules come under The Textiles Products (Indication of Fibre Content) Regulations? Tick the correct options.

A The fibre content only needs to be given if the fabric is a blend of more than one fibre.

B The correct chemical names must be used; not just trade names.

C Only synthetic and regenerated fibres need to be declared.

D Fibres must be listed in descending order; with the highest content fibre first.

E These regulations only apply to garments.

F The fibre content must be clearly stated on the label.

Flammability   AQA • OCR

3 All upholstered furniture must carry a fire label of some sort.
What wording should be used on the label if it is made from flameproof material.

A Fireproof

B Flameproof

C Fire resilient

D Flame resistant

4 Other than upholstered furniture, what type of product is governed by strict regulations relating to flammability?

Exam-Style Questions

Answer ALL the questions.

For questions **1–10**, choose answer **A**, **B**, **C** or **D**. Put a cross [X] in the box to indicate the answer you have chosen.

1 What is the name of this symbol?

A BSI Mark of Safety ◯

B Conformité Européenne Symbol ◯

C European Eco Label ◯

D Fairtrade logo ◯ *[1 mark]*

2 What does CAM stand for?

A Centre of Advanced Manufacture ◯

B Certificate of Assurance for Manufacture ◯

C Computer Automated Manufacture ◯

D Computer Aided Manufacture ◯ *[1 mark]*

3 Which is an example of a man-made fibre?

A Cotton ◯

B Silk ◯

C Viscose ◯

D Wool ◯ *[1 mark]*

4 What is 'one-off production'?

A A small number of products are made ◯

B A sample or individual product is made ◯

C A specific number of products are made ◯

D Products arrive just in time to be sold ◯ *[1 mark]*

5 What type of solution is cotton fabric placed into when a finish is applied using the 'mercerising' method?

   A   Bleach ◯   **B**   Silicone ◯

   C   Cellulose ◯   **D**   Hydroxide ◯   *[1 mark]*

6 What is 'virtual design'?

   A   A general term for computer software ◯

   B   A design that is never manufactured ◯

   C   A 3D representation of a product ◯

   D   A design specification ◯   *[1 mark]*

7 What is one of the purposes of a barcode?

   A   To keep track of stock in a business ◯

   B   To tell you whether the product is recyclable ◯

   C   To show how much money a company is making ◯

   D   To show what materials a product is made from ◯   *[1 mark]*

8 What method of decoration uses shapes that are stitched onto a background fabric?

   A   Quilting ◯   **B**   French seam ◯

   C   Appliqué ◯   **D**   Stencilling ◯   *[1 mark]*

9 What do you apply to the surface of the fabric in Batik?

   A   A mordant ◯   **B**   Binding agent ◯

   C   A pigment ◯   **D**   Hot molten wax ◯   *[1 mark]*

10 What type of paper is used for heat transfer printing methods?

   A   Tracing paper ◯   **B**   Sublimation paper ◯

   C   Transfer paper ◯   **D**   Printing paper ◯   *[1 mark]*

11 The table below shows the uses of some components and equipment.

Complete the table by giving the missing names and the uses of each piece of equipment or component.

Equipment /Component	Use
Screen printing frame and squeegee	
	To make marks on fabric before cutting or sewing.
	To finish off the edges of the material to prevent fraying.
Hook and loop fastening	

[4 marks]

12 a) What method of construction was used to produce the fabric show in the diagram below?

_____ *[1 mark]*

b) Is the **weft** direction shown by arrow A or B? _____ *[1 mark]*

c) Is the **warp** direction shown by arrow A or B? _____ *[1 mark]*

d) What type of machine would this fabric have been produced on?

_____ *[1 mark]*

13

a) What type of seam is shown in the diagram?

_____ *[1 mark]*

b) What type of specialist equipment is used to produce this seam?

_____ *[1 mark]*

c) What is the purpose of this seam?

_____

_____ *[1 mark]*

Exam-Style Questions

14 This table shows different methods of adding colour.

a) Complete the table sort by giving one advantage for each method.

Method	Advantage
BLOCK PRINTING	
STENCILLING	
DIGITAL PRINTING	
SCREEN PRINTING	

[4 marks]

b) What is the main disadvantage of screen printing?

_____

_____ [1 mark]

c) What type of fabric is suitable for heat transfer printing

_____ [1 mark]

15 a) Match the types of labels with the diagram below.

i) Gummed = ...

ii) Permanent = ...

iii) Swing ticket = ... *[3 marks]*

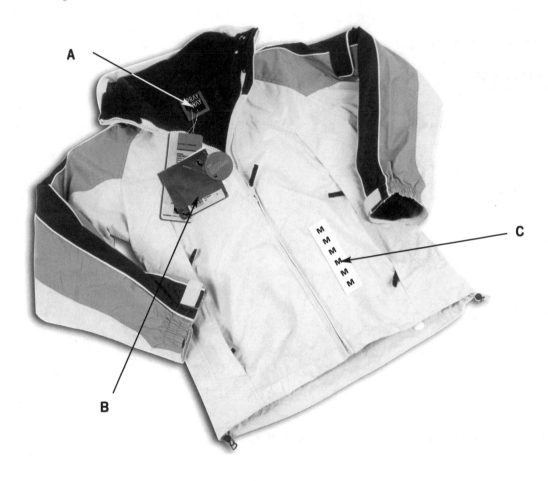

b) Name four things that you would expect to find on a garment label.

i) ....

ii) ....

iii) ....

iv) .... *[4 marks]*

Exam-Style Questions

16 **a)** Give three examples of **woven fabrics**.

1. .... [1]

2. .... [1]

3. .... [1]

[3 marks]

b) List three characteristics of woven fabrics and three characteristics of non-woven fabrics.

Woven Fabrics

1. .... [1]

2. .... [1]

3. .... [1]

[3 marks]

Non-Woven Fabrics

1. .... [1]

2. .... [1]

3. .... [1]

[3 marks]

17 **a)** List four combined properties of **polyester and cotton.**

1. .... [1]

2. .... [1]

3. .... [1]

4. .... [1]

[4 marks]

b) What is the advantage of mixing and blending fibres?

.... *[1 mark]*

18 You have been asked to design a reusable bag for a major supermarket chain, which is promoting their environmentally-friendly image.

The specification for the bag is that it must:
- be cheap to make
- be fashionable and aimed at teenagers and young adults
- be based on the theme of nature
- be safe to use
- use decorative techniques
- be strong to hold heavy shopping
- have two strong handles
- be suitable for one-off production in the classroom.

In the boxes on the next page, use sketches to show **two different** design ideas for a bag that meet the specification points above.

Use annotation and labelling to help explain parts of your design, where appropriate.

Marks will be given for:

- use of a natural theme   *[2 marks]*
- originality and quality of the design, including surface decoration   *[2 marks]*
- method of carrying or hanging the bag and use of new technologies   *[4 marks]*
- use of colour   *[2 marks]*
- use of fabrics and components.   *[2 marks]*

[Total of 12 marks per idea]

a) Research is usually carried out before design work begins. What are the two categories of research?

1. .... [1]

2. .... [1]

[2 marks]

b) Other than nature, name three possible sources of inspiration for designers.

1. .... [1]

2. .... [1]

3. .... [1]

[3 marks]

c) The boxes below are for your two design ideas.

Design Idea A

[12 marks]

Design Idea B

[12 marks]

d) Choose **one** of your design ideas for development.

Tick the appropriate box to show which idea you would choose.

Design Idea **A** ◯   Design Idea **B** ◯

Analyse and evaluate how the design idea you have chosen will appeal to a specific target market.

....

....

....

.... *[2 marks]*

e) Describe the following surface decoration techniques and explain how they might benefit your design ideas.

Appliqué

Description:

....

.... *[1 mark]*

Benefits:

....

.... *[1 mark]*

Embellishment

Description:

....

.... *[1 mark]*

Benefits:

....

.... *[1 mark]*

Exam-Style Questions

Quilting

Description:

....

....

[1 mark]

Benefits:

....

....

[1 mark]

f) Draw your design choice in the box below and show some development.
Remember to include annotation to explain the changes made.

Development of chosen design

[8 marks]

19 a) An environmentally-friendly alternative to reusable bags is to use recyclable bags. Explain what 'recyclable' means?

....

....

....

[1 mark]

b) i) What is the name of this symbol?

X%

.... *[1 mark]*

ii) What does 'X%' at the centre of this symbol mean?

.... *[1 mark]*

c) Explain the three types of recycling below:

i) Primary recycling

.... *[1 mark]*

ii) Secondary recycling

.... *[1 mark]*

iii) Chemical or Tertiary Recycling

.... *[1 mark]*

d) Name three ways that you can recycle your old clothes or textile products.

1. ....

2. ....

3. ....

[3 marks]

Exam-Style Questions

20 What type of production would be most suitable for producing your reusable bag if it was chosen by the supermarket? Explain your reasons

Type of Production

.... *[1 mark]*

Reasons

....

....

.... *[2 marks]*

21 Why would it be efficient to use ICT when designing the pattern pieces for the bag?

....

....

.... *[2 marks]*

22 Explain what is meant by the term 'colourways'.

....

.... *[2 marks]*

23 Complete the table by giving one use and one advantage for each piece of ICT equipment shown if it is used for design development.

	Use	Advantage
Digital Camera		
Scanner		
Spreadsheet		

[6 marks]

24 Below is an example of an interactive play mat for young babies.

a) i) Name the method that could be used to add padding to the mat to cushion a baby?

....

ii) What is the name of the material used between the layers of fabric for this method?

.... *[2 marks]*

b) Give five criteria that you would need to include on a design specification for a play mat.

1. ....

2. ....

3. ....

4. ....

5. ....
[5 marks]

c) What safety issues would you need to take into consideration when designing a play mat?

....

....

.... *[2 marks]*

25 a) Sketch **two initial ideas** for a play mat with a farm yard theme. Use some of the specification criteria you listed in question 24 b).

Design Idea A

[6 marks]

Design Idea B

[6 marks]

b) Choose **one** of your design ideas for development.

Tick the box to show the idea you would choose.

Design Idea **A** ◯   Design Idea **B** ◯

Draw and label a final design, showing some development.

Final and developed idea

[8 marks]

c) Add a special feature to your design using smart materials. The special feature needs to support learning through play.

Draw a diagram and explain where it would go and why?

Diagram of section of the mat

[3 marks]

Explanation:

_____

_____

_____

_____

[2 marks]

26 a) Give four methods of marketing that could be used to promote your playmat in a store.

1. _____

2. _____

3. _____

4. _____

[4 marks]

b) Many people now purchase products by **e-commerce**. Explain what this means.

....

....

.... *[1 mark]*

27 Name three safe components that could be used on the mat to attach removable parts?

.... *[1 mark]*

28 Name the following components and then give a possible use for each one on a baby mat.

[4 marks]

	Name	Use
		Used for decoration and to create different textures for the baby to touch and feel.
	Zipper	
		To secure the draw-string bag used for storing the mat.
	Braiding	

29 What does this symbol mean?

.... *[1 mark]*

30 Draw an ironing / pressing aftercare symbol below.

[1 mark]

31 a) What property of fabrics would the equipment below be used to test for?

.... *[1 mark]*

b) Label the test diagram.

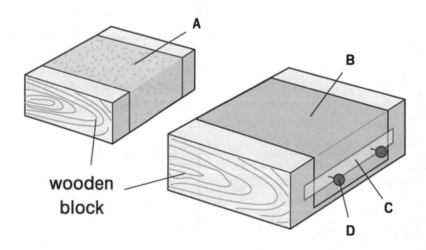

wooden block

A =

B =

C =

D =

[4 marks]

32 The 'design phase' of a project is also known as 'Pre-production'. Supply text for stages A and B to complete the flow diagram showing the processes that it is necessary to complete in this phase.

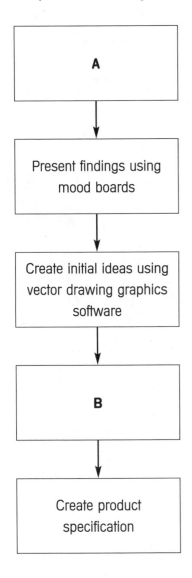

A = ...

....

....

B = ...

....

....

[2 marks]

33 What is a computerised lay plan?

....

....

.... *[2 marks]*

Notes

Notes